Love Monkey

for Freya

HarperCollins*Publishers*
77–85 Fulham Palace Road,
Hammersmith, London W6 8JB

www.harpercollins.co.uk

First published by HarperCollins*Publishers* 2010
2

A catalogue record of this book
is available from the British Library

ISBN 978 0 00 730745 6

Printed and bound in China by Leo Paper Products Limited

LOVE MONKEY

It was once the custom that every monkey would carve for himself a wooden HEART.

And the heart that Love Monkey carved was the most BEAUTIFUL of all.

Its contours were SOFT and rounded, like an ancient pebble sculpted by the oceans. Its surface was SMOOTH and shiny like liquid silk, and it shone as BRIGHT as a ruby in the desert sun.

"Take your hearts with you wherever you go," said their teacher. "NURTURE them as a mother nurtures her newborn baby. For when you want to GIVE of yourself fully, your heart is the only TRUE gift you will have."

That night, Love Monkey had a **DREAM**.

He dreamt of a monkey whose **SMILE** lit up his soul like sunshine. He held out his heart to her, so **RADIANT**, so splendid and so new. She took him in her arms and he felt truly, perfectly, at **PEACE**.

When Love Monkey awoke he resolved that, from that day forward, he would search for his Dream Monkey until he could stand before her and give to her his PERFECT heart.

He travelled
through deserts...

...and climbed
over mountains.

He trekked
across forests...

...and sailed
many oceans.

Love Monkey looked after his heart as best he could, but the storms that he endured on his travels CHIPPED away at its surface and each new adventure reshaped it.

By the time he arrived on the last distant shore, his heart was so CHANGED by the patina of time that it barely resembled his old heart at all.

And then, he saw her.

Standing before him, as radiant and as **BEAUTIFUL** as the sunshine, was his Dream Monkey.

At first he could not speak. But then, from somewhere deep inside himself, he found a voice.

"I have travelled the world over to **FIND** you, and to **GIVE** you my heart," he said.

"But now that I am finally with you, I see how FOOLISH I have been. You are so beautiful, so perfect. And my heart that was once so smooth, so BRIGHT and so new is now not something that I could even bring myself to SHOW you," and he turned to go.

"Let me see it," said Dream Monkey. She took his heart and held it up to the **LIGHT**.

"Nothing to me is more **BEAUTIFUL**. Every fissure tells a story. Every blemish makes you more **REAL**. All my life I have been waiting for a **HEART** like this; a heart that speaks the **TRUTH**.

"Come here," she said. "I have something for you too."

In her hand was a tiny, **GOLDEN** heart. It was as worn and as scratched as **Love** Monkey's own... and it was the most **PRECIOUS** thing that he had ever seen.

Love Monkey put his arms around her and they HELD each other for a long, long time.

"I shall **TREASURE** this heart for as long as I live," said Dream Monkey, running her fingers over its ridged and dimpled surface.

Then they looked into each other's eyes and, feeling the **JOY** of **TRUTH** in their souls for the first time, they began to laugh.

And often they sit together still, **HOLDING** each other's hearts in their **WARM** hands, lifting them to the light... and **LAUGHING**.

Always laughing.

THE END